INTEGRATING
PRIMITIVE REFLEXES
THROUGH PLAY AND EXERCISE

AN INTERACTIVE GUIDE TO THE
SPINAL GALANT REFLEX

FOR PARENTS, TEACHERS
AND SERVICE PROVIDERS

KOKEB GIRMA MCDONALD, OTR/L
OCCUPATIONAL THERAPIST REGISTERED AND LICENSED

ISBN – 978-1-7342143-6-9 (E-book)
ISBN - 978-1-7342143-7-6 (Paperback)

Illustrator – Alex Lopez
Editor – Bernice Martin Delcorde
Formatter – Jen Henderson at Wild Words Formatting

DEDICATION

MY HUSBAND

Thank you for your love and support. Your dedication to making a positive difference in the world continues to inspire me daily. I love the journey we are on together.

PARENTS AND CAREGIVERS

To all parents and caregivers of children with special needs. You take on more than most, and continuously strive to better the future of your children, often without the support you and your children need. I hope this book eases your challenging journey and offers you a useful tool for incorporating helpful exercises in your home. Remember, you are not alone!

TEACHERS

You are one of our children's primary influencers and game changers. Helping you to create a safe and effective classroom for all children is my main goal. Outside of the home, you have the most impact on our children's development.

FELLOW SERVICE PROVIDERS

Lastly, to my fellow occupational therapists and service providers, you work hard to meet the needs of your clients, often not seeing the fruits of your labor. Working alongside you has been a great privilege and is what pushes me to continue finding effective solutions to our clients' and their families' needs every day. Together we can make a difference!

FREE GIFT

Thank you for purchasing our book

As a special thank you, we'd love to gift you with FREE companion resources to help you on your journey!

DOWNLOAD NOW

RITP.INFO/SPINAL -GALANT-BOOK

Transform your Treatment Plans ANYWHERE, ANYTIME!

Access to 100+ exercises to address retained reflexes

Collect exercises together into easy to access playlists

Share playlists with other app users!

Kid friendly easy-to-follow videos and instructions right in your pocket!

Access to exclusive learning videos by Kokeb Mcdonald, OTR/L & Author

DOWNLOAD OUR APP NOW

RITP.INFO/APP

LEARN MORE

RITP.INFO/CERTIFICATION

Are you a Service Provider ready to grow?

Explore our Reflex Integration Through Play™ Certification Program!

 Say Hello to...

- Refining and expanding your clinical skills to effectively address the most complex developmental delays
- Broadening your professional and business opportunities available to you as a therapist
- Having a done-for-you treatment and at-home plan highly targeted to treat children with developmental delays

The Program Includes

In-Depth Courses & Training

Live Support Calls

Collaborative Community

Access to Mobile App

Done-For-You Treatment Plans

Step-by-Step Play-Based Exercises

American Occupational Therapy Association

Approved Provider

LEARN MORE

RITP.INFO/FAMILY

Skyrocket your Child's Progress at HOME!

As a parent, do you...

- See developmental challenges in your child and don't know where to start?
- Want to accelerate your child's therapy program?
- Feel overwhelmed with at-home movement plans and want to make it more fun?

We want to support you with our Reflex Integration Through Play™ Family Bundle!

Our Family Bundle Includes:

Hours of training on play-based reflex integration tailored to a home environment

In-depth on-demand course covering retained reflexes & their impact on your child

Access to our Mobile App (100+ exercise instructions!)

Access to a private membership community

Bring Reflex Integration Through Play™ to Your School!

Are you an educator looking to provide fun movement breaks & sensory diet programs for your students?

Your Students Will...

- Grow in their energy levels
- Improve their attention span and academic performance
- Progress in their social skills and physical abilities

LEARN MORE

RITP.INFO/SCHOOL

TABLE OF CONTENTS

PREFACE

Welcome to *An Interactive Guide to* Spinal Galant Reflex, the fifth book in the series, *Integrating Primitive Reflexes Through Play and Exercise*, part of Reflex Integration Through Play™. I hope you'll find these exercises simple, fun and useful.

If this is your first experience with this series, please also check out the **first four books in the series on the Moro Reflex, Asymmetrical Tonic Neck Reflex (ATNR), Symmetrical Tonic Neck Reflex (STNR), and Tonic Labyrinthine Reflex (TLR).** Much of the information in this book, such as the introduction, reflex descriptions and definitions, is similar to that in the previous books. Working first on the Moro Reflex, and alongside the ATNR, STNR, and TLR, may also be essential for success with the exercises for the Spinal Galant Reflex included in this book. If you have read the other books, understand primitive reflexes and their benefits, and simply want to focus on the Spinal Galant Reflex, you can skip to Chapter 2, and begin the program.

Many parents spend time reading about research and findings but are left more confused and overwhelmed than they were before, as much of the information available is geared toward professionals. What most parents need is a practical guide that relies on research yet is written in terms they can understand and easily put to use. After publishing the first book in this series on the Moro Reflex, and later on the ATNR and STNR, I received positive feedback from several parents, teachers and service providers who said that the simple, step-by-step instructions were helping them. They also reported that they had been looking for a simple guide with clear instructions but, until now, had not been able to find one. If you are one of these parents, you know what it feels like to balance your work, life, parental duties, and still make sure you are providing the best possible support for your child's developmental needs. This book is mainly for you.

The books in this series are not presented in any specific order. If you choose, you can work on many reflexes at the same time or in any sequence. However, if you suspect your child may have Moro Reflex retention, for example, I highly recommend you start with that reflex. Since the Moro Reflex affects all of our senses, including our fight and flight response, it is best to start calming the nervous system before tackling the challenge of integrating other reflexes, which can be stressful; however, you do not need to have the Moro Reflex fully integrated to begin working on other reflexes.

While you may begin working on any reflex—or multiple reflexes—as you first utilize this series, it is essential that you know the retention of one reflex often leads to the retention of another reflex. It is not always clear, however, which reflex is dominating the body at a given time. **To be safe, I recommend screening for and working on *all* primitive reflexes with a trained specialist.** With the results of comprehensive screening, you will be better informed and able to implement these guidebooks for optimal results. In the meantime, you can safely incorporate these fun games and exercises into your clinic, classroom or home routine in a way that makes sense for you and your client, and observe your client's performance. I chose these specific exercises because they are easy to implement and allow for easy observation of the retained reflex pattern when it is present in the body. Plus, they are fun, and parents can participate in at-home exercises, allowing for healthy play. A win-win for all!

I hope you'll find the information and exercises in this book helpful on your journey to support the development of the clients with whom you work. Read our newsletter, find free resources and training at https://integratingreflexes.com/signup, and join our growing community on Facebook at: https://www.facebook.com/groups/1629371470539695. There you'll find discussions and further information about Reflex Integration Through Play™.

Kokeb Girma McDonald, OTR/L
California, 2023

INTRODUCTION

A child's treatment program should be a collaboration between parents and therapists. Therapists can guide a child's development better if they partner with the parents in the treatment plan. The best intervention is one that carries over into the home. A weekly therapy session without the parents' collaboration and education will not be as effective on a child's development. It is a team approach, like rowing a canoe; you will get to your destination faster and with less energy expenditure when everyone on the boat works together.

Since parents are their child's first teachers, and are the most likely to motivate and influence them, they can incorporate the therapist's recommendations throughout the day. By doing that, they can (1) provide needed repetition and (2) easily discern what interventions are working well and give feedback to the therapist. This process not only helps to achieve faster results but also reduces the number of therapy sessions needed and the total cost. However, when parent-therapist collaboration is weak, the therapist can only rely on data collected during an individual session in a controlled environment, instead of having a better understanding of the child's development and skills that were carried over to the child's natural settings. This lack of data can lead to termination of a potentially effective intervention and a waste of time, energy and money. Children need a lot of repetition; if the child does not have enough carryover, there will be inconsistency, confusion, lack of interest and frustration.

As a working parent, I can testify that it is hard to come home from a busy work day and still manage to do therapeutic exercises with your child. You are tired, and your child is tired. The last thing you probably want to do is start an activity your child is going to fight you over. Even as a trained and experienced pediatric occupational therapist, I am challenged when I make these home exercises a chore for my child and less motivated when I do not fully understand the reason behind the activities. Children learn through play. What my child wants is to spend time with me and play. It takes creativity and guidance to set up a home program that can be easily carried over to the house. The best ones are those that are fun, explorative and playful for the child and you.

In this book, I will provide simple, play-based and step-by-step therapeutic exercises that are focused on the Spinal Galant Reflex. This book is different from the others since it contains advanced exercises that can be done with adults as well as children.

Primitive reflexes are involuntary movement patterns that are present at birth and should have been integrated before the child reaches 12 months. When these reflexes do not stay dormant, they will begin to affect the way the child processes the environment and responds to it. We usually can see these responses by the way the child reacts emotionally (behavior) and moves (physically). The best way to integrate these reflexes is by recreating infantile activities the child should have mastered to integrate the system in the first place. These exercises give the child a second chance to reintegrate and rewire the brain-body connection.

The goal of this handbook is to try and meet the following needs:

1. Understanding the Spinal Galant Reflex: Resources and Basic Therapeutic Exercises

    Provide resources for new occupational therapists to understand the Spinal Galant Reflex, including basic therapeutic exercises that aid in its integration, and information on the symptoms and behaviors that may accompany a retained Spinal Galant Reflex.

2. Step-by-Step Exercises for Integration of the Spinal Galant Reflex

    Offer straightforward, step-by-step exercises that explain the rationale behind each activity. The book contains a range of therapeutic exercises that challenge or assist in integrating the Spinal Galant Reflex, with varying difficulty levels that can be adjusted to suit individual treatment sessions.

3. Involving Caregivers: Home-Based Exercises and Tracking Charts

   Train and involve caregivers in the treatment process, as effective intervention requires carry-over into the home environment. The book includes exercises that can be easily performed at home, facilitating education and repetition, resulting in faster results. Caregivers can monitor progress using the tracking charts provided in the appendix of this book.

This program is not intended as medical advice and should be done with the help of a trained service provider.

This book should not be used to diagnose or replace other therapeutic reflex integration programs.

CHAPTER 1

PRIMITIVE REFLEXES AND THEIR BENEFITS

THE BENEFITS OF REFLEXES

Primitive reflexes are involuntary movement patterns controlled by the brain stem and are executed without reaching the cortical or conscious part of the brain. All primitive reflexes emerge in utero, are present at birth, and should be integrated between 6 – 12 months after birth. Several primitive reflexes emerge in utero and integrate before the child reaches about 12 months of age. Some of the reflexes include, but are not limited to, the Moro Reflex, Palmar Reflex, Rooting Reflex, Asymmetrical Tonic Neck Reflex, Spinal Galant Reflex, Tonic Labyrinthine Reflex and Symmetrical Tonic Neck Reflex.

These primary reflexes are all necessary for the infant's first-year survival and during its transition into the world. Together they help the infant go through the birth canal, take its first breath, withdraw from hazardous stimuli, urinate, creep, grasp, lift its head, open its mouth, suck and swallow, and kick. All these movements are involuntary, and the infant cannot control or know what it is doing. Each primitive reflex has its own benefit, and is a building block to the infant's future movements and how it perceives the world via its senses. When the infant is in utero and after birth, it does not know what it needs or how to get it, it just has primitive reflexes. Instinctively the infant responds to the world via these primitive reflexes.

As the infant grows, a healthy and typically developing brain allows the infant to benefit from these primitive reflexes, and gradually begins to integrate the reflexes to develop voluntary and purposeful movements. If there are any pregnancy and/or birthing complications, genetic abnormality or injuries to the brain, or incorrect functioning, primitive reflexes may stay active in the body. If primitive reflexes remain active, there will always be involuntary movements or responses present in the body. These reflexive responses will appear in the patterns in which the child moves, behaves or reacts to stimuli. Moreover, as the child continues to grow, he or she may begin to perceive the world in an immature way, and behavioral challenges may follow when primitive reflexes are actively present.

Primitive reflexes are succeeded by postural reflexes so retained primitive reflexes will affect a child's development. Postural reflexes are mature patterns of responses that control balance, motor coordination and sensory-motor development. As a result, it will be challenging to work on a child's postural reflexes, for instance, without first going back and making sure the brain has integrated the primitive reflexes. When a child's brain is healthy and developing normally, maturity and growth become automatic. The child goes through movement patterns that are considered natural and instinctive while assisting the brain in integrating primitive reflexes. We usually see a disturbance in the brain when the child either does not go through the milestones or skips them all together. For example, a child moves from sitting to walking, skipping the crawling phase, which is essential. In fact, every stage is essential, and the best way we can integrate these reflexes is by following the natural process, which is mimicking activities and movements that are missed or done incorrectly in early stages, and letting the brain experience it so it can rewire itself.

In this book, we will discuss a primitive reflex called the Spinal Galant Reflex.

CHAPTER 2

WHAT IS THE
SPINAL GALANT REFLEX?

A. ONSET AND PATTERNS OF THE SPINAL GALANT REFLEX

The Spinal Galant Reflex is a reflex pattern that is present in utero, present at birth and continues to be present until close to 9 months of age. Spinal Galant Reflex is an involuntary reaction in response to the tactile stimulation to one or both sides of the sides of the back. When one side of the back is stroked from top to bottom, it causes the body to bend toward the direction of the touch. When both sides of the lower back are touched (stroked), it stimulates urination.

The Spinal Galant Reflex emerges in utero, is present at birth, and integrates around five – nine months of age. In utero, the Spinal Galant Reflex helps develop auditory perception—the ability for the fetus to respond to sound waves. Before birth, it assists the fetus in turning its head down to prepare for the birthing process. In conjunction with the Asymmetrical Tonic Neck Reflex (ATNR) and Symmetrical Tonic Neck Reflex (STNR), it influences a cross-lateral movement, which later helps the child to learn to twist, turn, crawl, stand and walk. As the child continues to develop, the Spinal Galant Reflex continues to assist with spine flexibility, stability, posture and control.

Image #1: Spinal Galant Reflex Pattern

SENSORY TRIGGER ONE: BOTH SIDES TRIGGER

1st Trigger: Stroking one side of the lower back

Motor responses include:

- Side (lateral) flexion of the body toward the side being stroked

- Leg abduction (lift to the side being stroked)

- Head might turn toward the side being stroked

- Hip lifts up (toward the touch)

SENSORY TRIGGER TWO: BOTH SIDES TRIGGER

2nd Trigger: Simultaneously <u>stroking both sides</u> of the lower back

Motor responses include:

- Confusion: When both sides get activated, the brain can get confused and the body may respond by freezing or a stuck response.

- Stress response

  o Might cry, show distress or emotional response

  o Stimulates urination

B. BENEFITS OF THE SPINAL GALANT REFLEX

BIRTHING PROCESS

The Spinal Galant Reflex works together with other primitive reflexes, such as the Asymmetrical Tonic Neck Reflex (ATNR), to facilitate the descent of the infant through the birth canal during delivery. More precisely, the Spinal Galant Reflex aids in positioning the baby's head downward in preparation for the birthing process. Additionally, it plays a role in the maturation of the vestibular system (Image #2) as the child develops.

BLADDER CONTROL

Stimulating the Spinal Galant Reflex can trigger the bladder muscles to contract involuntarily, resulting in urinary urgency and/or leakage. If the Spinal Galant Reflex persists beyond infancy, it may lead to bladder control problems in children, such as bedwetting or daytime urinary incontinence.

VESTIBULAR SKILLS

The **Vestibular System** is a sensory organ, located in both inner ears (Image #2 below), and gives feedback to the brain regarding the head position, motion, balance, posture and spatial relation. Similar to the visual and auditory systems, any reflex pattern that moves the head, including the Spinal Galant Reflex, helps develop the vestibular system.

Image #2: Location of the vestibular system

Auditory figure-ground Is the ability to hear specific sounds in a noisy environment. For example, a child will be able to respond to your call amid all the noise at the playground or while watching TV. **Auditory localization** is the ability to perceive and locate from where a sound is coming. For example, a child can turn toward the sound and locate the source. The Spinal Galant reflex helps with the early development of hearing high and low sound waves while in utero.

Image #3: Head turns toward a source of sound

Binaural hearing is the ability to hear with both ears equally. **Receptive language** refers to the ability to understand and interpret sounds, words and sentences accurately. For a more in-depth understanding, screening, and treatment options for receptive language and speech, please consult a speech therapist.

PELVIC MOBILITY

Pelvic mobility is the ability of the pelvis to move through its full range of motion in all directions. The pelvis is a complex structure comprising several bones, including the sacrum, coccyx and hip bones, which are connected by ligaments and muscles.

The pelvis can move in several directions, including:

1. **Anterior tilt:** When the front of the pelvis moves forward and the back of the pelvis moves backward, creating a forward curve in the lower back.

2. **Posterior tilt:** When the back of the pelvis moves forward and the front of the pelvis moves backward, creating a backward curve in the lower back.

3. **Lateral tilt:** When one side of the pelvis moves upward and the other side moves downward, creating a side bend in the lower back.

4. **Rotation:** When one side of the pelvis moves forward and the other side moves backward, creating a twist in the lower back.

Adequate pelvic mobility is essential for proper pelvic floor function, optimal hip-joint health and posture. The Spinal Galant Reflex directly affects the lateral tilt and rotation movement of the pelvis, and the connected muscles, joints and ligaments.

SPINE DEVELOPMENT AND FLEXIBILITY

Spinal mobility is the ability of the spine to move freely and efficiently through its full range of motion. Proper spinal mobility is crucial for maintaining good posture, balance, and overall physical function. Various factors influence spinal mobility, including genetics, injury and disease.

The back-and-forth movement of the hips caused by the Spinal Galant Reflex helps strengthen and activate the spinal muscles on one side of the spine while relaxing the muscles on the other side. This movement pattern is important for promoting spinal mobility and flexibility.

POSTURE

Posture is how we align and hold our spine with our shoulders, head, pelvis, hips and feet. There are two types of postures: dynamic and static. **Dynamic posture** is how the body is aligned while in motion (e.g., walking, running, swimming, etc.). **Static posture** is how the body is aligned when there is no motion (e.g., sitting, standing, sleeping). The Spinal Galant is one of the primitive reflexes that directly influences both dynamic and static postures.

The Spinal Galant Reflex influences the pelvis and spine alignment. To have proper posture, agonist and antagonist muscles must work in unison to keep the head and spine aligned. If the Spinal Galant Reflex persists beyond infancy, specifically if one side is stronger than the other, it can lead to a lack of spinal alignment. This is because the constant rotation of the hips can cause an imbalance in the muscles supporting the spine. This imbalance can lead to poor posture, limited range of motion, pain and possible scoliosis.

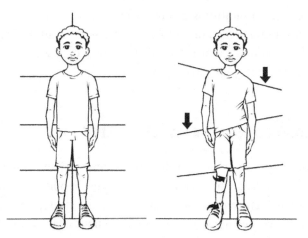

Image #4: Posture affected by active Spinal Galant Reflex on one side

AN OVERVIEW OF THE BENEFITS OF THE SPINAL GALANT REFLEX

- Assists with the birthing process

- Assists with cross-lateral movements in early development, such as crawling and walking

- Assists with head-righting, specifically with lateral movements

- Influences muscle tone, neck control and core stability developments

- Influences muscles and ligaments between pelvis, hip and lower back

- Influences the connection between legs and the core

- Influences spine flexibility and postural control

- Influences the vestibular system via the inner ear and proprioceptive system

- Assists with the cross-lateral movements (e.g., crawling, standing and walking)

- Assists and influences bladder and bowel control

- Contributes to whole body movement coordination

- Assists with proper space orientation and sense of direction (e.g., right and left, up and down)

- Contributes to the coordination of opposing lateral core muscles (i.e., agonist and antagonist muscles)

- Influences the auditory processing system (e.g., high and low frequencies)

- Influences the vestibular system, which affects balance, spatial orientation and posture

- Assists with fine motor skills and eye-hand coordination

- Assists with speech and language development

- Influences the learning process and skills

- Influences static and dynamic postures

- Influences gross motor coordination

- Influences focus and attention

- Indirectly influences cognitive skill by influencing auditory and visual skills (e.g., focusing and concentration)

C. RETAINED SPINAL GALANT REFLEX: SIGNS, SYMPTOMS AND BEHAVIORS

When the Spinal Galant Reflex is active (retained) in the body past the integration stage, it creates delays in a child's fine motor and gross motor skills, bladder control, pelvis stability and mobility, vestibular skills, auditory processing, proprioception, and focus and attention skills. Below is a list of signs and symptoms that may indicate a retained Spinal Galant Reflex.

SIGNS AND SYMPTOMS OF A RETAINED SPINAL GALANT REFLEX

GROSS AND FINE MOTOR DEVELOPMENT CHALLENGES:

- Lack of coordination in both fine motor and gross motor skills
- Low endurance and fatigue
- Decreased interest and motivation in gross motor activities
- Dislikes physical activity
- Poor balance
- Poor motor planning and coordination
- Poor muscle tone; fatigues easily
- May have difficulty with cross-lateral skills causing coordination problems
- Awkward gait and movement

PELVIC FLOOR AND BLADDER CONTROL ISSUES:

- Poor bladder control, bedwetting and incontinence
- May develop irritable bowel syndrome (IBS)

- May have weak pelvic floor muscles

- Difficulty with potty training; it might take a long time

- Digestive issues

POSTURE AND STABILITY CHALLENGES:

- Difficulty maintaining proper seated posture, often appearing slouchy and uncomfortable

- Might have tight hips and appears stiff (e.g., hard time stretching legs, hips and spine)

- Slight or exaggerated upward rotation of the hip

- Scoliosis in cases where the retention is stronger on one side

- Difficulty maintaining balance and posture

- Uneven hips/pelvis or scoliosis of the spine

- Weak muscle tone; slouched

- Poor muscle tone and overall posture

- Prefers to work standing than seated

- Poor head control

**Image #5: Example of static posture (i.e., standing)
with retained Spinal Galant Reflex**

TACTILE ISSUES:

- Tactile hypersensitivity or defensiveness

- Discomfort or aversion to being touched around the waistline

- May appear itchy and squirmy (e.g., constantly fixing shirt, bending side to side or touching self)

- May dislike tags or tight clothing around waist

- Hypersensitivity and pain in the lumbar area

- Refusal to wear certain types of textured clothes (e.g., picky and rigidity to wearing a variety of clothing textures)

AUDITORY AND VISUAL SKILLS CHALLENGES:

- Difficulty with speech and articulation

- Poor auditory processing (e.g., challenges with multiple instructions and verbal learning)

- Difficulty with auditory focusing

- Difficulty with visual focusing

ATTENTION AND CONCENTRATION CHALLENGES:

- Difficulty holding still and concentrating

- Fidgety behavior and inability to sit still

- Poor concentration and attention span

- Hyperactivity

- Inability to sit still or maintain proper posture in a chair; sometimes referred to as "ants in their pants" due to their constant movement

- Difficulty processing information due to continuous fidgeting and distractibility (challenges with concentration and focus)

- Fidgeting and squirming from stimulus touching the back (ex., clothing, chair backs)

- Mental fatigue

- May have challenges with memory or thinking skills that require focus

- Hyperactive due to constant stimulation of the reflex by clothing; the child might release agitation in "disruptive ways"

- Always appears on the move/in motion

- Preference to do homework lying on the floor to prevent irritation

CHAPTER 3

TESTING AND SCREENING FOR SPINAL GALANT REFLEX

There are specific testing methods that trained therapists and service providers use to check for a retained Spinal Galant Reflex. This book, however, is not designed to teach any one testing method. This screening list should only be used to gather data, not to determine a specific diagnosis. In addition, while not a formal evaluation method, I have compiled a symptoms and behavioral checklist (Table #1) to be filled out by parents and service providers during the screening process.

A. SYMPTOMS AND BEHAVIORAL CHECKLIST: SPINAL GALANT REFLEX

Observe the child and circle the number that best represents the severity of the symptoms you observe. You can **use this checklist first to gather data for an initial baseline and then again 6–12 weeks after the start of intervention to assess progress**.

TESTING AND SCREENING FOR SPINAL GALANT REFLEX

	Symptoms and Behaviors						
1	Poor muscle tone and overall posture (e.g., stooped posture; slouched)	0	1	2	3	4	5
2	Fidgety behavior and inability to sit still	0	1	2	3	4	5
3	Poor concentration and attention span	0	1	2	3	4	5
4	Poor seated posture; prefers to work standing	0	1	2	3	4	5
5	Poor auditory processing (e.g., challenges with multiple instructions and verbal learning)	0	1	2	3	4	5
6	Hyperactivity	0	1	2	3	4	5
7	Inability to sit still or maintain proper posture in a chair; sometimes referred to as "ants in their pants" due to their constant movement	0	1	2	3	4	5
8	Poor bladder control, bedwetting and/or incontinence	0	1	2	3	4	5
9	May develop irritable bowel syndrome (IBS)	0	1	2	3	4	5
10	Poor seated posture on floor (e.g., constantly moving)	0	1	2	3	4	5
11	May have weak pelvic floor muscles	0	1	2	3	4	5
12	Lack of coordination in both fine motor and gross motor skills	0	1	2	3	4	5

13	Weak core muscle stability and balance	0	1	2	3	4	5
14	Poor head control (e.g., may be tilted to the side)	0	1	2	3	4	5
15	Low endurance and fatigue	0	1	2	3	4	5
16	Poor balance and stability	0	1	2	3	4	5
17	Decreased interest and motivation in gross motor activities	0	1	2	3	4	5
18	Discomfort or aversion to being touched around the waistline	0	1	2	3	4	5
19	Difficulty with speech and articulation	0	1	2	3	4	5
20	Difficulty holding still, concentrating; inattention (e.g., may have ADD or ADHD tendencies)	0	1	2	3	4	5
21	Difficulty maintaining proper seated posture; often appearing slouchy and uncomfortable	0	1	2	3	4	5
22	Difficulty with multi-step-movement instructions and activities (e.g., skipping, jumping and balancing games, etc.)	0	1	2	3	4	5
23	Slower working speed (e.g., fatigues easily and functions slower than most)	0	1	2	3	4	5
24	Difficulty and frustration playing sports	0	1	2	3	4	5

25	Awkward gait and movement	0	1	2	3	4	5
26	Tactile hypersensitivity or defensiveness	0	1	2	3	4	5
27	Always appears on the move	0	1	2	3	4	5
28	Tendency to be disorganized and forgetful	0	1	2	3	4	5
29	May appear itchy and squirmy (e.g., constantly fixing shirt or bending side to side)	0	1	2	3	4	5
30	Might have tight hips (e.g., hard time stretching legs, hips and spine)	0	1	2	3	4	5
31	Digestive issues	0	1	2	3	4	5
32	Slight or exaggerated upward rotation of the hip (e.g., scoliosis in cases where the retention is stronger on one side)	0	1	2	3	4	5
33	Difficulties maintaining balance and posture (vestibular)	0	1	2	3	4	5
34	Fidgeting and squirming from stimulus touching the back (ex., clothing, chair backs)	0	1	2	3	4	5
35	May have challenges in memory or thinking skills that require focus	0	1	2	3	4	5
36	May dislike tags or tight clothing around the waist	0	1	2	3	4	5

37	Hypersensitivity and pain in the lumbar area	0	1	2	3	4	5
38	Hyperactivity due to constant stimulation of the reflex by clothing; the child might release agitation in "disruptive ways"	0	1	2	3	4	5
39	Refusal to wear certain types of textured clothes (e.g., picky and rigidity to wearing varieties of clothing)	0	1	2	3	4	5
40	Difficulty processing information due to continuous fidgeting and distractibility (challenges with concentration and focus)	0	1	2	3	4	5
41	Preference to do homework lying on the floor to prevent irritation	0	1	2	3	4	5
42	Mental fatigue	0	1	2	3	4	5

Table #1: Symptoms and Behavior Checklist for Spinal Galant Reflex

Note: Usually, one retained reflex leads to the retention of other reflexes. To be safe, work on all of the primitive reflexes. **Before working with a child, go through the symptoms checklist, and rate the severity of the symptoms or behaviors** on a scale of 0–5, 0 being "not seen" to 5, being "seen all the time."

You can use the following exercises as part of the screening process **to determine if further testing is needed.** Inability to perform the following exercises well might be a sign of a retained Spinal Galant Reflex.

B. SCREEN 1: LOWER BACK STROKE (ALL FOURS)

MATERIALS: Pencil or brush

INSTRUCTIONS:

Image #6: Screening for retained Spinal Galant Reflex

1. Position client on hands and knees.

2. Using the back of the pencil, stoke down one side of the back from top to bottom. Do not touch the spine.

OBSERVATION

When the side of the back is stroked:

- Whole side bends toward the stroke

- Shoulder bends toward the hips

- Hips bend toward the shoulder

- Might twist and sit on the floor

- Refusal to continue with the screening after a couple of strokes

- Uncomfortable and itchy

Note: These movements can be slight, so make sure to observe carefully.

B. SCREEN 2: LOWER BACK STROKE (SIDELYING)

INSTRUCTIONS:

1. Position clients on their side.

2. Using the back of the pencil, stoke down from top to bottom, on the side of the back that is facing up. (Do not touch the spine.)

OBSERVATION

When the side of the back is stroked:

- Whole side bends toward the stroke

- Shoulder bends toward the hips

- Hips bend toward the shoulder

- Head might lift toward the side of the stroke

CHAPTER 4

ADDRESSING RETAINED SPINAL GALANT REFLEX

A. INTERVENTION AND TREATMENT PLANNING

A number of interventions may be appropriate for those with a retained Spinal Galant Reflex. One of the simplest ways to help integrate primitive reflexes is by mimicking early-childhood movement patterns. In addition, we can incorporate exercises to target muscles that contribute to the specific reflex pattern.

The Spinal Galant Reflex significantly impacts various aspects of physical functioning, including core muscle control, hip flexibility, pelvic stability and control, posture, spine mobility, motor coordination and auditory processing. This book focuses on exercises that target the muscles and joints directly impacted by the Spinal Galant Reflex.

The exercises compiled in this book are for those receiving occupational therapy and other reflex integration treatments. In the back of this book, I have added advanced exercises, preferably best used by a skilled Pilates Instructor. If you are not a trained specialist, please consult with one. The exercises can be used in clinics, schools, homes and gyms. Once you have introduced the activities, you can use them as a daily home program to be followed by caregivers and clients, and as a movement break in a school setting with the help of a trained professional.

The age groups with which you can use these exercises vary from preschoolers to adults. You do not need to do every exercise listed in this book since it is not appropriate for everyone. Please use your clinical judgment, client history, and the level of support clients require before you introduce an activity. The exercises give the reader an overall understanding of Spinal Galant movement patterns and the types of exercises challenging for those with a retained Spinal Galant Reflex.

It is challenging to trigger only one reflex when using a play-and-exercise approach to treatment. Therefore, as a clinician, you must know the other reflex patterns, and whether they are triggered and affect the client's performance. **To best serve clients, try the exercises from simple to hard before adding more challenging tasks that might frustrate them.**

> **Note:** A correct visual processing skill is necessary for learning. It is crucial that a trained practitioner screens a child to rule out possible retained reflexes and visual skill delays that may affect learning.

To help incorporate auditory processing skills and responses, we will use cues, such as clapping, snapping, counting, or the use of a metronome. A **metronome** is a device used by musicians that marks a tempo in beats-per-minute. You can use a physical metronome device or download a mobile app. The use of a metronome will increase the challenge of the exercise and, at the same time, help you focus more on the child and less on giving verbal cues. When choosing a tempo, if the child tends to go very fast, start with a faster tempo, and gradually slow it down. If the child tends to go very slowly, start with a slower tempo, and gradually increase the speed. Do not get frustrated. Meet children at their skill level.

B. ACCOMMODATIONS

A child with a retained Spinal Galant Reflex may have delayed motor coordination skills, postural control, flexibility, bladder control, attention and concentration difficulties. For a classroom or workstation, choose one or more of the following accommodations to meet the child's needs:

1. Allow working in different positions. Do not focus on the upright seated position when you are focusing on education. Allow the child to be comfortable and not expend a lot of energy to maintain postural balance. Instead, provide a variety of options, such as:

   a. Standing at a desk to write.

   b. Lying down on the floor to read.

   c. Using a therapy ball as a chair.

   d. Using a slanted board to elevate working materials and keep the head straighter.

2. Break down verbal instruction:

   a. Provide written instruction for review.

   b. Have the child repeat the first instruction before adding additional instructions.

3. For movement activities, accommodate right- and left-side confusion by providing the following:

a. Visual cues to help differentiate the right and left sides of the body.

b. A picture or video to imitate.

c. Tactile cues to help feel the parts of the body.

d. A breakdown of the steps.

4. Provide movement breaks from the exercises described in this book to help promote Spinal Galant Reflex integration.

5. Do not force games and sports; the child may not be ready for advanced movements without breaking down the steps.

6. Provide flexibility for bathroom breaks. You can have a code you can use with a child to let you know they need a bathroom break.

C. EXERCISES TO PROMOTE SPINAL GALANT REFLEX

The exercises below can be used in the order you think is best for your client. Follow the order presented here or combine the exercises with others during your session. The manner in which you utilize the exercises depends on the environment, the client's state, and the materials you have on hand. For example, make the activities fun and exciting when working with younger children, but feel free to create more of a workout session with older children and adults. Avoid activities that create frustration and anxiety. As much as possible, try to make the exercises fun and enjoyable. For kids who are younger and refuse to cooperate, incorporate the use of positive reinforcement or rewards to encourage participation. Most of the exercises in this book will target core muscles, hip flexibility, pelvic stability and control, posture, spine mobility and motor coordination.

Note: The following exercises might challenge more than one of the primitive reflexes, including the Spinal Galant, encourage bilateral coordination, balance, spatial awareness, posture, hip mobility and flexibility, visual skills, and auditory and motor planning skills. Use the additional modifications and accommodations for exercises that many find difficult.

1) SNOW ANGEL

MATERIALS: Mat

INSTRUCTIONS:

*Add metronome to work on timing and auditory processing

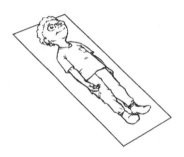

1. Lie down on your back, with legs together and arms by your sides.

2. Simultaneously, open both arms and legs, then bring them back to the starting position.

3. Repeat 5–7 times, slowly.

SAME SIDES

4. Simultaneously, open the right arm and the leg, then bring them back to the starting position.

5. Simultaneously, open the left arm and the leg, then bring them back to the starting position.

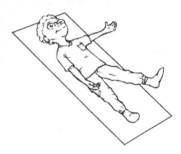

6. Repeat 5–7 times, slowly.

OPPOSITE SIDES

7. Simultaneously, open the right arm and the left leg, then bring them back to the starting position.

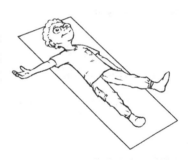

8. Simultaneously, open the left arm and the right leg, then bring them back to the starting position.

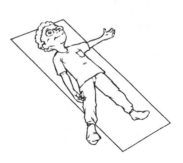

9. Repeat 5–7 times, slowly.

GOALS

1. Motor planning and timing

2. Tactile (desensitization)

3. Visual skills (peripheral vision, visual fixation, visual tracking)

4. Body awareness

5. Right- and left-side discrimination

6. Bilateral coordination

7. Strength and posture

8. Upper-body and lower-body differentiation

9. Spatial orientation

10. Auditory processing

POSITIVE SIGNS

- ☐ Able to coordinate arms and legs at the same time

- ☐ Able to differentiate right and left sides of the body

- ☐ Able to move with the metronome

NEGATIVE SIGNS

- ☐ May appear uncomfortable and become fidgety

- ☐ Confusion; might need additional support to identify parts of the body

- ☐ Inability to coordinate movements

- ☐ Moves arms but not legs or vice versa

- ☐ Movement overflow (other parts of the body might be moving)

MODIFICATIONS

- Provide physical support (i.e., tactile cues to help them visualize their body)

- Provide visual cues to help with right- and left-side discrimination

2) TAIL WAG

MATERIALS: Mat

INSTRUCTIONS:

*Add metronome to work on timing and auditory processing

1. Begin on all fours (hands and knees) with elbows straight, maintaining a straight spine and neck position.

2. Lift one foot slightly, while keeping the knee on the floor. This is your "tail."

3. Turn head and foot toward one side of the body; hold. If possible, look at the foot.

4. Turn head and foot the other way, and look at the other foot; hold. Note: Look over the shoulder; keep spine and neck parallel to the floor.

5. After 3–5 turns, switch legs and repeat.

GOALS

1. Lateral flexibility and strength

2. Pelvis flexibility

3. Spine mobility and flexibility

4. Head alignment and control

5. Upper-body and lower-body differentiation

6. Core stability and strength

7. Bilateral coordination

8. Body awareness

9. Balance and control

10. Motor planning and timing

11. Vestibular input

POSITIVE SIGNS

☐ Maintains head control and balance while twisting from side to side

☐ Able to keep spine parallel to the floor (i.e., no sagging back or dropped neck)

☐ Maintains shoulder stability and control

☐ Able to keep the non-moving body stable

☐ Able to twist to one side by bringing shoulder and hips together

NEGATIVE SIGNS

- ☐ Head drops or back may arch

- ☐ Fidgety and constantly on the move

- ☐ Appears uncomfortable and itchy (e.g., may be fixing shirt constantly)

- ☐ Unable to maintain balance and coordinate movement

- ☐ Unable to switch from right to left

- ☐ Confusion and frustration

- ☐ Delayed upper-body and lower-body coordination

- ☐ Lack of endurance

- ☐ Might feel dizzy or nauseous

3) HIP CIRCLES ON THERAPY BALL

MATERIALS: Therapy ball

INSTRUCTIONS:

1. Sit on a therapy ball, keeping a neutral spine and feet flat on the floor.

2. Keep still for 10-15 seconds and maintain balance.

NEXT

3. While maintaining stable feet, move hips from side to side.

4. Repeat 3-5 times.

5. Move hips back and forth.

6. Repeat 3-5 times.

7. Without lifting feet off the floor, while maintaining balance, do hip circles toward 12 o'clock; move clockwise from 1

o'clock to 6 o'clock and all the way back to 12 o'clock, making sure you are hitting each number.

8. Repeat 3-5 times.

9. Reverse the direction, move hips counterclockwise, from 12 o'clock to 11 o'clock all the way to 6 o'clock, 3 o'clock and back to 12 o'clock, making sure to hit each number.

10. Repeat 3-5 times.

Note: This exercise may involve a small movement, yet it engages numerous muscles. The emphasis is not on the size of the circles but on the ability to isolate the specific muscles that drive the hip movement while maintaining balance throughout the body. Thus, the slower and more regulated the motion, the greater the benefits.

GOALS

1. Core stability and control

2. Later flexibility and strength

3. Neck control and strength

4. Upper-body and lower-body differentiation

5. Right- and left-side discrimination

6. Head control

7. Balance

8. Spatial awareness

9. Postural alignment

10. Hip flexibility

POSITIVE SIGNS

- ☐ Ability to distinguish hip movements from movements of other body parts

- ☐ Ability to move the pelvis in various directions

- ☐ Ability to maintain stability and control

- ☐ Ability to keep both feet planted firmly on the ground

- ☐ Ability to keep the upper and lower body steady and stable

NEGATIVE SIGNS

- ☐ Easily falls off the ball with any movement

- ☐ Movement initiated from other parts of the body and not hips

- ☐ Inability to move the hips separately

- ☐ Excessive movement in other parts of the body instead of the pelvis

4) SUPINE HEEL TAP

MATERIALS: Mat

INSTRUCTIONS:

*Add metronome to work on timing and auditory processing

1. Lie on your back, with knees bent and arms straight, next to your body.

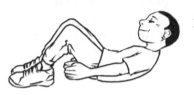

2. Crunch up, lifting head, being careful to keep the neck straight.

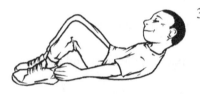

3. While keeping both feet flat on the floor, swing the upper body to the left and tap the back of the left heel.

4. Then swing the upper body to the right and tap the back of the right heel.

5. Continue alternating for 5–7 times.

GOALS

1. Core strength and control

2. Later flexibility and strength

3. Tactile (desensitization)

4. Pelvis control

5. Lower body strength and stability

6. Neck control and strength

7. Upper-body and lower-body differentiation

8. Right- and left-side discrimination

9. Head control

10. Vestibular input

POSITIVE SIGNS

☐ Able to coordinate movements

☐ Able to keep feet flat on the floor while the upper body is moving

☐ Able to attempt to reach toward the feet

☐ Able to only move from the upper body

☐ Able to keep hips flat on the floor

NEGATIVE SIGNS

☐ Discomfort and fidgety

☐ Unable to maintain balance

☐ Difficulty with movement

☐ Difficulty keeping hips stable

☐ The hips or the lower body might move toward the side of the upper body that is moving

Note: Do not do this exercise if there is neck pain.

5) BACK CRAWL

MATERIALS: Smooth surface

INSTRUCTIONS:

1. Lie on your back, with knees bent and both feet on the floor.

2. Bring your arms off the floor and curl up.

3. While maintaining the forward curl, crawl backward for 10 feet using only your feet and your lower back. (Do not use your arms.)

4. Repeat 3–5 times.

GOALS

1. Core stability and strength

2. Tactile (desensitization)

3. Posture and balance

4. Bilateral coordination

5. Motor planning and timing

6. Head and shoulder control

7. Spatial orientation

8. Visual skill (e.g., peripheral, fixation, tracking)

9. Body awareness

10. Right- and left-side discrimination

11. Upper-body and lower-body discrimination and coordination

12. Vestibular input

POSITIVE SIGNS

☐ Able to motor plan and coordinate smooth movement patterns

☐ Able to keep the forward curl while crawling backward

☐ Able to differentiate lower body and upper body

☐ Maintains balance and head control

NEGATIVE SIGNS

☐ Unable to coordinate and execute movement

☐ May become fidgety and uncomfortable

☐ Difficulty maintaining head control

☐ May use the arms to help with movement

☐ Neck and shoulder tension

☐ Low endurance and balance

6) THERAPY BALL MASSAGE

MATERIALS: Small therapy ball

INSTRUCTIONS:

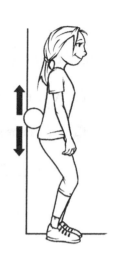

1. Balance a ball on the wall, using only hips and back.

2. Move the ball up and down against the wall while flexing and extending your knees to massage the back.

3. Repeat 10 times.

4. Shift weight from one leg to the other while moving the ball from side to side against the wall to massage the back.

5. Repeat 10 times.

GOALS

1. Tactile (desensitization)

2. Posture and balance

3. Motor planning and timing

4. Right- and left-side discrimination

5. Spatial orientation

6. Body awareness

POSITIVE SIGNS

☐ Able to motor plan and coordinate smooth movement patterns

☐ Maintains balance and head control

☐ Able to maintain balance while rocking from left to right

☐ Able to keep feet in one place

NEGATIVE SIGNS

☐ Unable to coordinate and execute movement

☐ Fidgety and squirmy

☐ May drop the ball constantly

☐ Discomfort and becomes itchy (e.g., scratching back)

☐ Aversion to activity and refusal

7) ELBOW TO HIP SQUEEZE

MATERIALS None

INSTRUCTIONS:

*Add metronome to work on timing and auditory processing

1. Stand with right hand on right shoulder and left hand on left shoulder. Or follow the image below and keep your hands on the back of the head. Maintain a straight spine.

2. Simultaneously, raise the right heel up and bring the elbow toward the right hip.

3. Repeat 10 times.

4. Go back to the starting position.

5. Simultaneously, raise the left heel up and bring the elbow toward the left hip.

6. Repeat 10 times.

GOALS

1. Lateral flexibility

2. Hip flexibility

3. Shoulder and scapula flexibility

4. Core stability and strength

5. Spine mobility and flexibility

6. Body awareness

7. Balance and control

8. Motor planning and timing

9. Upper-body and lower-body differentiation

10. Spatial orientation

POSITIVE SIGNS

☐ Able to coordinate the upper and lower body together

☐ Able to keep the opposite foot on the floor

☐ Able to lift hips and heels up at the same time

☐ Able to keep spine perpendicular to the floor

☐ Able to keep straight knees

NEGATIVE SIGNS

- ☐ Confusion and frustration

- ☐ Difficulty coordinating the upper and lower body together

- ☐ May flex the spine forward instead of side bends

- ☐ May lift leg off the floor and flex knee

MODIFICATIONS

- Start by moving one part of the body at a time

  - o Move only the hips

  - o Move only the shoulders and scapula

  - o Then, combine upper and lower body together

8) PLANK TO SIDE TAPS

MATERIALS: Mat

INSTRUCTIONS:

*Add metronome to work on timing and auditory processing

1. Start in a high plank position with feet together.

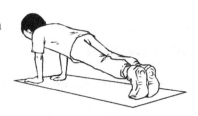

2. Maintain stability in your upper body as you move one leg out and tap the floor. (Originate movement from your hips and keep your knees straight.)

3. Alternately "tap" each foot slightly to the side while maintaining a straight back.

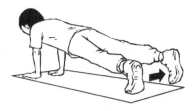

4. Repeat 7-10 times in each direction.

GOALS

1. Bilateral coordination

2. Motor planning and timing

3. Spatial orientation

4. Body awareness

5. Right- and left-side discrimination

6. Posture and balance

7. Core stability and strength

8. Shoulder stability and control

9. Head control and stability

10. Upper-body and lower-body differentiation

POSITIVE SIGNS

☐ Able to coordinate movement patterns

☐ Able to maintain balance

☐ Able to keep head and spine parallel to the floor

☐ Able to move lower body while maintaining balance

NEGATIVE SIGNS

☐ Unable to coordinate movement

☐ Unable to maintain posture; falls

☐ Hips may drop; unable to keep level to the floor

☐ Unable to keep knees straight; knees may keep bending

☐ Difficulty differentiating right and left sides of the body

☐ Upper body moves with the lower body

☐ The head or the upper body might move toward the leg that is moving

VARIATION

- Elbows on the floor

9) ROLLING LIKE A BALL

MATERIALS: Mat

INSTRUCTIONS:

1. Start by pulling knees toward your body and create a "C" shape with the spine. Eyes should gaze down.

2. Begin by lifting the feet off the floor and balancing for a few seconds. Maintain tension between the front and back muscles.

3. Roll back all the way to the upper back and shoulders, then roll forward.

4. Repeat 5–7 times.

GOALS

1. Tactile (desensitization)

2. Core stability and strength

3. Posture and balance

4. Bilateral coordination

5. Motor planning and timing

6. Head and shoulder control

7. Spatial orientation

8. Visual skill (e.g., peripheral, fixation, tracking)

9. Body awareness

10. Upper-body and lower-body discrimination and coordination

11. Vestibular input

POSITIVE SIGNS

☐ Able to motor plan and coordinate smooth movement patterns

☐ Able to keep a "C" spinal curve while rocking back and forth

☐ Organizes and differentiates upper and lower body

☐ Maintains balance and head control

NEGATIVE SIGNS

☐ Unable to coordinate and execute movement

☐ Rocks side to side and unable to maintain balance

☐ Difficulty maintaining head control

☐ Unable to keep a "C" spinal curve while rocking back and forth

☐ Fidgety and squirmy

☐ Neck and shoulder tension

☐ Discomfort

☐ Aversion to activity and refusal

10) HULA HOOP

MATERIALS: Appropriately sized hula hoop

INSTRUCTIONS:

1. Place the hula hoop on the floor, step inside, then bring it up to hip level.

2. Swing the hula hoop around the midsection, rotating the hips to keep it spinning around the body.

> **Note:** Make sure you continue practicing as long as it remains enjoyable. Incorporating music into the activity can enhance your level of interest and motivation.

GOALS

1. Pelvis flexibility

2. Body alignment

3. Core stability and strength

4. Bilateral coordination

5. Body awareness

6. Balance and control

7. Motor planning and timing

8. Spatial orientation

POSITIVE SIGNS

☐ Able to differentiate hip movement

☐ Able to maintain interest to improve with activity

☐ Able to differentiate right and left sides of the body (i.e., rotate hips to either side)

NEGATIVE SIGNS

☐ Confusion and frustration

☐ Moves the entire body

☐ Discomfort and dislikes how the hula hoop feels on body

☐ Maybe fidgety and "itchy"

☐ Gives up easily

11) BRIDGE HIP DROP

MATERIALS: Mat

INSTRUCTIONS:

1. Lie on your back, with knees bent, arms to the side.

2. Lift hips to a bridge pose, with feet planted flat on the floor.

3. Lift one leg then slowly lower hips to the floor. Maintain the lift of the hips on the opposite side.

4. Hold for 5-7 seconds.

5. Return to the starting position and repeat with the other leg.

6. Hold for 5-7 seconds.

7. Repeat 5–7 times.

GOALS

1. Core stability and control

2. Hip flexibility

3. Pelvis control

4. Upper-body and lower-body differentiation

5. Right- and left-side discrimination

6. Lower body strengthening and control

7. Balance and stability

POSITIVE SIGNS

☐ Able to coordinate movement on both sides of the body

☐ Able to keep the opposite hip stable

☐ Able to keep a neutral spine

☐ Able to keep upper body relaxed

NEGATIVE SIGNS

☐ Unable to coordinate movement

☐ Both hips may drop to the floor

☐ Difficulty with right and left sides

☐ Low endurance and fatigue

☐ Stress on neck muscles or pain when lifting head toward the opposite side

12) PELVIC CLOCK

MATERIALS: Mat and small therapy ball

INSTRUCTIONS:

WARMUP (PREWORK)

1. Lie on your back, with knees bent, arms loosely out to the side, and feet flat on the floor.

   *Imagine you are lying on an imaginary clock.

2. Gently rock your pelvis back, toward the head, 12 o'clock position.

3. Rock your pelvis toward your feet, 6 o'clock.

4. Repeat 3–5 times.

5. Gently rock the pelvis side to side, toward 3 o'clock and 9 o'clock.

   *Be careful not to overextend while rocking. These should be small and gentle movements.

6. Repeat 3–5 times.

7. Without overextending the back, tilt the pelvis toward the 12 o'clock position and move clockwise from 1 o'clock to 6 o'clock, and all the way back to 12 o'clock, making sure you are hitting each number.

8. Repeat 3-5 times.

9. Reverse the direction, move the pelvis counterclockwise, from 12 o'clock to 11 o'clock all the way to 6 o'clock, 3 o'clock and back to 12 o'clock, making sure you are hitting each number.

10. Repeat 3-5 times.

GOALS

1. Pelvic stability and flexibility

2. Lateral flexibility

3. Hip flexibility

4. Core stability and strength

5. Body awareness

6. Balance and control

7. Motor planning and timing

8. Spatial orientation

9. Right- and left-side discrimination

10. Upper-body and lower-body discrimination

POSITIVE SIGNS

☐ Ability to distinguish hip movements from movements of other body parts

☐ Ability to move the pelvis in various directions

☐ Ability to maintain stability and control

☐ Ability to keep both feet planted firmly on the ground

☐ Ability to keep the upper and lower body steady and stable

NEGATIVE SIGNS

☐ Inability to move the pelvis properly

☐ Excessive movement in other parts of the body instead of the pelvis

☐ Tension in the neck and shoulders

☐ Facial grimaces and movement overflow

☐ Confusion and restlessness

VARIATIONS

- If using a therapy ball is too difficult, do not use a ball. Using a small therapy ball will give you increased range of motion but is not necessary.

- For an added challenge, try lying with a small therapy ball under the sacrum (center of the pelvis).

13) RESISTANCE BAND SIDE STEPS

MATERIALS: Resistance band

INSTRUCTIONS:

*Add metronome to work on timing and auditory processing

1. Begin standing, feet shoulder width apart, with a resistance band around both thighs.

2. Slowly walk to the side by moving the outside leg, then move the other leg, for 5–7 steps.

3. Walk back in the same way.

GOALS

1. Balance and stability

2. Bilateral coordination

3. Hip stability and strength

4. Core stability and strength

5. Right- and left-side discrimination

6. Bilateral coordination

7. Body awareness

8. Spatial orientation

9. Lower body strength

POSITIVE SIGNS

- ☐ Able to maintain upper body balance and control while moving

- ☐ Able to maintain tension on the band while moving

- ☐ Able to motor plan and complete movements on either side

- ☐ Able to keep straight spine posture and core stability

NEGATIVE SIGNS

- ☐ Unable to maintain tension on band (i.e., band may fall down)

- ☐ Low endurance and flexibility

- ☐ Fatigues easily

- ☐ Poor balance and trunk control

VARIATIONS

- For more resistance and strengthening, try lowering the resistance band to the ankles.

- To increase the level of challenge and work on the glutes, try bending the knees (i.e., a half squat position). You can have the band either at the thighs, shins or ankles.

14) FIRE HYDRANT

MATERIALS: Mat

INSTRUCTIONS:

1. Begin on all fours (hands and knees), with elbows straight, while maintaining a straight spine and neck position.

2. Slowly raise one leg out to the side, keeping the knee bent, then return it to the starting position. Keep the back and neck in the starting position.

3. Raise and lower the other leg.

4. Repeat 5–7 times.

GOALS

1. Lower body flexibility and strength

2. Pelvis (hip) flexibility and stability

3. Head control

4. Upper-body and lower-body differentiation

5. Core stability and strength

6. Shoulder strength and stability

7. Spatial awareness

8. Body awareness

9. Balance and control

10. Motor planning and timing

POSITIVE SIGNS

☐ Able to differentiate lower body

☐ Able to keep upper body stable during exercise

☐ Able to have lateral flexibility without twisting

☐ Able to raise legs up without scapula and shoulder movement

☐ Able to keep spine parallel to the floor

NEGATIVE SIGNS

- ☐ Difficulty maintaining balance

- ☐ Upper body moves with the lower body

- ☐ Excessive tension on shoulders and arms

- ☐ Difficulty raising legs up to the side

- ☐ May collapse to the floor

- ☐ Fidgety and constantly on the move

- ☐ The head or the upper body might move toward the leg that is moving

- ☐ Spine may twist toward the side of the raised leg

15) THERAPY BAND SIDE BEND

MATERIALS: Long resistance band

INSTRUCTIONS:

1. Firmly hold the resistance band with both hands and step on it with both feet. The therapy band should have some resistance when pulled with the hands.

2. Stand up straight, continuing to hold the band.

3. Bend slowly to one side, while maintaining tension on the band. Hold for 1 second.

4. Repeat the bend on the other side.

5. Repeat 10 times.

GOALS

1. Spine flexibility and mobility

2. Core stability and strength

3. Body awareness

4. Balance and control

5. Motor planning and timing

6. Hand grasp strength

7. Head and neck control

8. Upper-body and lower-body differentiation

9. Vestibular input

POSITIVE SIGNS

☐ Able to maintain tension on the band at all times

☐ Able to maintain straight elbows and relaxed upper body

☐ Able to only move from the waist

NEGATIVE SIGNS

☐ May over arch or extend the spine

☐ Unable to maintain tension on the band

☐ Difficulty switching from side to side

☐ Might feel dizzy or nauseous

16) SEATED CHAIR SIDE BEND

MATERIALS: Chair

> **Note:** This exercise would be **well suited for individuals who use a wheelchair** and may not have full access to their leg muscles.

INSTRUCTIONS:

1. Sit on the edge of a chair.

2. While keeping hips level, bend down to one side, touching the outside of the foot.

3. Return to the starting position and repeat on the other side.

4. Repeat 10 times.

GOALS

1. Core stability and control

2. Spine flexibility and strength

3. Neck control and strength

4. Upper-body and lower-body differentiation

5. Right- and left-side discrimination

6. Head control

7. Balance

8. Vestibular input

POSITIVE SIGNS

☐ Able to stretch on both sides

☐ Able to keep hips stable

☐ Able to keep neutral spine arch

☐ Able to maintain good head control with the spine

NEGATIVE SIGNS

☐ Fidgety

☐ Might lift off the chair

☐ Slouches (e.g., C curve)

☐ Excessive spine arching

- ☐ Head might over stretch or unable to maintain balance

- ☐ Feet might lift

- ☐ May fall off chair

- ☐ Stress on neck muscles or pain when lifting head toward the opposite side

- ☐ Might feel dizzy or nauseous

VARIATION

- Twist, as you bend down, to touch the inside of the foot on the opposite side. This exercise can have similar benefits as the Cross Crawl exercise. (Refer to the ATNR book, exercise #22.)

17) SEATED FLOOR SIDE BEND

MATERIALS: None

INSTRUCTIONS:

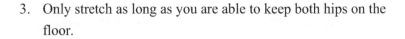

1. Start in a seated position, with legs criss crossed.

2. Side bend to the left by placing the right hand over the head and reach toward the left.

3. Only stretch as long as you are able to keep both hips on the floor.

4. Hold for 3-5 seconds.

5. Reverse the direction and stretch to the right.

6. Repeat 3-5 times.

VARIATION

- To increase flexibility, straighten one leg instead of criss-crossing legs.

GOALS

1. Core stability and control

2. Spine flexibility and strength

3. Neck control and strength

4. Upper-body and lower-body differentiation

5. Right- and left-side discrimination

6. Upper-body and lower-body flexibility

7. Head control

8. Balance

9. Spatial awareness

10. Postural alignment

11. Vestibular input

POSITIVE SIGNS

☐ Able to stretch on both sides

☐ Able to keep hips stable

☐ Able to keep neutral spine

☐ Able to maintain good head control with side movements

NEGATIVE SIGNS

☐ Fidgety

☐ Might lift off the floor

☐ Slouches (e.g., C curve)

☐ Head might over stretch or unable to maintain balance

☐ Stress on neck muscles or pain when lifting head toward the opposite side

☐ Might feel dizzy or nauseous

18) STANDING LEG STRETCH

MATERIALS: None

INSTRUCTIONS:

1. Start in a standing position.

2. Lift one knee up and hold the shin.

3. Hold the stretch for 5-7 seconds.

4. Switch to the other side.

5. Repeat 3-5 times.

VARIATION

- Raise one knee and keep it lifted for 2-3 seconds, then gradually release the shin and maintain equilibrium for 5-7 seconds.

GOALS

1. Core stability and control

2. Hip flexibility and strength

3. Posture and balance

4. Upper-body and lower-body differentiation

5. Balance and strength

6. Body awareness

POSITIVE SIGNS

☐ Able to maintain straight back and posture

☐ Able to bring knees up for good hip mobility

☐ Able to lift hands while maintaining a straight back

NEGATIVE SIGNS

☐ Unable to stretch with a straight back

☐ Slouches (e.g., C curve)

☐ Pain and discomfort

19) SUPINE LEG STRETCH

MATERIALS: Mat

INSTRUCTIONS:

1. Lie on the floor with the back flat.

2. Lift one knee up off the floor and bring it toward the chest.

3. Hold the stretch for 5-7 seconds.

4. Switch to the other leg.

5. Repeat 3-5 times.

GOALS

1. Hip flexibility and strength

2. Tactile (desensitization)

3. Upper-body and lower-body differentiation

4. Body awareness

POSITIVE SIGNS

- ☐ Able to keep the opposite leg on the floor

- ☐ Able to bring knees up for good hip mobility

NEGATIVE SIGNS

- ☐ Unable to stretch without bending the opposite leg

- ☐ Fidgety

- ☐ Pain and discomfort

20) SIDE JACKKNIVES

MATERIALS: Mat

INSTRUCTIONS:

1. Lie down on one side, hips stacked, with legs and feet in a straight line with the back.

2. Place the top of the hand on the back of the head with the elbow pointing up.

3. Lift one leg and bring the upper body toward the feet.

4. Bring your elbow toward your knee as you lift your upper body and leg off the ground.

5. Hold for 2-3 seconds and then slowly lower yourself back down to the starting position.

6. Repeat 5–7 times.

7. Repeat on the opposite side.

Note: This is an **advanced exercise** so it is important to keep the core engaged throughout the exercise and to avoid arching the back. You can bend your knees slightly if you are having trouble keeping your legs straight. Additionally, you can modify the exercise by bending your legs at the knee and bringing them up to your chest instead of holding them straight.

GOALS

1. Core stability and strength

2. Bilateral coordination

3. Motor planning and timing

4. Spatial orientation

5. Body awareness

6. Right- and left-side discrimination

7. Posture and balance

8. Shoulder stability and control

9. Head control and stability

10. Upper-body and lower-body differentiation

POSITIVE SIGNS

- ☐ Able to keep spine in the same plane (i.e., frontal plane) the entire time

- ☐ Able to motor plan smooth movement

- ☐ Able to maintain head control

NEGATIVE SIGNS

- ☐ Unable to coordinate and execute movement

- ☐ Unable to maintain balance

- ☐ Difficulty maintaining head control

- ☐ Fidgety and squirmy

- ☐ Neck and shoulder tension

MODIFICATIONS

- Bend legs at the knee and bring them up to the chest instead of holding them straight.

- Bend elbow and rest head on hand.

21) WINDSHIELD WIPERS

MATERIALS: Mat

INSTRUCTIONS:

1. Lie on back, with knees bent and stacked on top of the hips, and arms loosely out to the side.

2. Slowly lower bent knees toward the floor on one side, as long as you can keep the upper body flat on the mat.

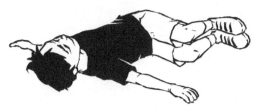

3. Bring the legs back to the starting position.

4. Repeat on the other side of the body.

5. Repeat 5–7 times.

GOALS

1. Core stability and strength

2. Tactile (desensitization)

3. Bilateral coordination

4. Motor planning and timing

5. Spatial orientation

6. Body awareness

7. Right- and left-side discrimination

8. Shoulder stability and control

9. Upper-body and lower-body differentiation

POSITIVE SIGNS

☐ Able to motor plan smooth movement

☐ Able to keep both legs together to move from side to side

☐ Able to only move from the lower body

☐ Able to keep shoulders and neck relaxed

NEGATIVE SIGNS

☐ Unable to coordinate and execute movement

☐ Difficulty keeping both legs together

☐ Fidgety and squirmy

☐ Neck and shoulder tension

☐ Back might arch

22) RESISTANCE EXERCISE ON HANDS AND KNEES

MATERIALS: None

INSTRUCTIONS:

1. Start on hands and knees. Wrist is under the shoulder, knees are under the hips and head is parallel to the floor.

2. Twist from the waist and bring the shoulder and hips toward each other. Hold for 2-3 seconds.

3. Twist to the opposite side and hold for 2-3 seconds.

4. Repeat 5-7 times.

VARIATION

- When working with someone, you can provide light tactile feedback by placing a hand on one side of the scapula (shoulder blade) and the other hand on one of the hips. Invite the person to twist toward your hand as you provide light resistance. Have them hold for 5-7 seconds.

- Do the same on the opposite side.

GOALS

1. Core stability and strength

2. Lateral stretching and flexibility

3. Tactile (desensitization)

4. Bilateral coordination

5. Motor planning and timing

6. Spatial orientation

7. Body awareness

8. Right- and left-side discrimination

9. Shoulder stability and control

10. Upper-body and lower-body differentiation

11. Vestibular input

POSITIVE SIGNS

☐ Smooth and coordinated movement pattern

☐ Able to maintain balance

☐ Able to keep head parallel to the floor

☐ Able to push against the active resistance

NEGATIVE SIGNS

☐ Difficulty differentiating right and left sides of the body

☐ Difficulty coordinating upper and lower body at the same time

☐ Confusion and frustration

☐ Difficulty with the active resistance exercise

23) ARMY CRAWL

MATERIALS: None

INSTRUCTIONS:

*Add metronome to work on timing and auditory processing

1. Lie flat on the floor.

2. Lift the left arm and the right leg; move forward while the opposite arm and leg stabilize the body.

3. Pull yourself forward, and simultaneously shift weight to the left.

4. Keep head parallel to the floor and facing forward.

5. Lift the right arm and the left leg; move them forward while the opposite arm and leg stabilize the body.

6. Pull yourself forward, and simultaneously shift weight to the opposite side.

7. Crawl forward 15-20 feet.

GOALS

1. Bilateral coordination

2. Motor planning and timing

3. Crossing the midline

4. Spatial orientation

5. Visual skill (peripheral vision, visual fixation, visual tracking)

6. Body awareness

7. Right- and left-side discrimination

8. Posture and balance

9. Stability and strength

10. Upper-body and lower-body coordination

POSITIVE SIGNS

☐ Smooth and coordinated movement pattern

☐ All four limbs coordinate simultaneously; no lagging

☐ Able to keep head straight and looking forward

☐ Able to keep head facing forward

NEGATIVE SIGNS

☐ Difficulty preventing the head from moving toward the twist

☐ Not using one side of the body (e.g., prefers to move using one side of the body and neglects the other)

☐ Difficulty differentiating right and left sides of the body

☐ Difficulty coordinating upper and lower body at the same time

☐ Confusion and frustration

MODIFICATIONS

- Give physical cues by either placing the correct arm and leg on the floor or tapping (touching) the side that needs to move.

- Use visual cues (e.g., use stickers on hands, and place the same colored sticker on the arm and leg that should move together).

- Practice crawling on hands and knees.

24) CRAWL WITH BEANBAG

MATERIALS: Weighted beanbag or toy

INSTRUCTIONS:

*Add metronome to work on timing and auditory processing

1. Tape a straight line on the floor.

2. Start on hands and knees, and place a weighted beanbag or toy on the lower part of the back.

3. Crawl forward, focusing the gaze slightly forward while watching the line on the floor and not dropping the chin or beanbag/toy.

4. Crawl forward for about 10-25 feet.

5. Crawl backward for about 10-15 feet.

GOALS

1. Bilateral coordination

2. Motor planning and timing

3. Tactile (desensitization)

4. Crossing the midline

5. Spatial orientation

6. Visual skills (peripheral vision, visual fixation, visual tracking)

7. Body awareness

8. Right- and left-side discrimination

9. Shoulder stability and strength

10. Balance and stability

POSITIVE SIGNS

☐ Able to motor plan and coordinate smooth movement patterns

☐ Understands and executes movement

☐ Able to keep the spine straight, not drooping or wiggling, and remains parallel with floor

☐ Able to crawl on a straight line

☐ Able to follow a metronome without frustration

NEGATIVE SIGNS

☐ Unable to crawl by following the line

☐ Unable to coordinate, balance, or keep the spine parallel to the floor

☐ Frustration with metronome and unable to slow down to match movement with sound

☐ Body wiggles around (e.g., side bending, squirmy, etc.)

VARIATIONS

- Use a metronome to work on auditory skills and timing.

- Crawl forward and backward with the same side of the body (i.e., right arm and right leg move together, and left arm and left leg move together).

- Crawl forward and backward contralaterally, with different sides of the body (i.e., right arm and left leg move together, and left arm and right leg move together).

25) DRIVING A CAR

MATERIALS: None

INSTRUCTIONS:

1. Start seated on the floor, with legs straight, back straight and both arms at shoulder height.

2. Initiate movement from the legs and hips, and scoot forward by twisting the upper body slightly.

3. Continue alternating between your right and left sides as you move forward for approximately 10 feet.

4. Return to your starting position by scooting backward using the same alternating movements.

GOALS

1. Core strength and control

2. Later flexibility and strength

3. Pelvis control

4. Lower body strength and stability

5. Upper-body and lower-body differentiation

6. Right- and left-side discrimination

POSITIVE SIGNS

☐ Able to coordinate movements

☐ Able to maintain core stability (i.e., neutral spine position)

☐ Able to alternate from right to left with adequate spine twist

☐ Able to move forward and backward

NEGATIVE SIGNS

☐ Unable to maintain neutral spine position

☐ Discomfort and fidgety

☐ Difficulty with movement

☐ May scoot from only one side and unable to shift to the opposite side

☐ Slouched posture

☐ Difficulty keeping arms parallel to the floor

26) TWIST JACKS

MATERIALS: None

INSTRUCTIONS:

*Add metronome to work on timing and auditory processing

1. Begin by placing one foot ahead of the other, maintaining a comfortable distance between them; position the arms similarly, and rotate the torso toward the leg in front.

2. Jump and quickly switch the foot positioning so the other foot is in front. Simultaneously, rotate your arms to the opposite side of the body.

3. Repeat the process, alternating between the two sides.

4. Repeat 10 times.

GOALS

1. Core strength and stability

2. Later flexibility and strength

3. Upper-body and lower-body coordination

4. Right- and left-side discrimination

5. Bilateral coordination

6. Motor planning

7. Vestibular input

8. Balance

POSITIVE SIGNS

☐ Able to coordinate movements

☐ Able to maintain balance

☐ Able to alternate from right to left with adequate spine twist

NEGATIVE SIGNS

☐ Difficulty moving opposite sides of the body

☐ Might side bend instead of twist

☐ Discomfort and confusion

☐ Fidgety

MODIFICATIONS

- Scissor Jumps (Refer to the ATNR book, exercise #24.)

- Cross Crawl (Refer to the ATNR book, exercise #22.)

27) BICYCLE CURLS

MATERIALS: None

INSTRUCTIONS:

*Add metronome to work on timing and auditory processing

1. Start with a flat back on the floor, with knees bent and hands on the back of the head.

2. Bring hands on the back of the head up and curl up. Bring both knees up.

3. Twist the upper body to the left and tap the left knee with the right elbow.

4. Then, twist the upper body to the right and tap the right knee with the left elbow.

5. Maintain flexion of the body while you repeat 7–10 times.

GOALS

1. Core stability and strength
2. Tactile (desensitization)
3. Posture and balance
4. Bilateral coordination
5. Motor planning and timing
6. Crossing the midline
7. Spatial orientation
8. Visual skill (e.g., peripheral, fixation, tracking)
9. Body awareness
10. Right- and left-side discrimination

POSITIVE SIGNS

☐ Able to motor plan and coordinate smooth movement patterns

☐ Understands and executes movement independently

☐ Differentiates right and left sides of the body

☐ Maintains balance and upright posture

NEGATIVE SIGNS

☐ Discomfort and fidgety

☐ Unable to coordinate and execute movement

☐ Difficulty twisting to the opposite side (e.g., same side might move together)

28) SEATED HIP STRETCH

MATERIALS: None

INSTRUCTIONS:

1. Start in a seated position on the floor, with knees bent and heels on the floor.

2. To keep your back straight, bend your knees as much as required while maintaining a straight posture.

3. Grab the ankles/legs with both hands and hold the stretch for 8-10 seconds.

4. Release the stretch and repeat 3-5 times or as long as desired.

5. If able, straighten the knees a few inches, as long as the back remains straight; repeat the stretch.

VARIATION

- While maintaining a straight back and stable body, lift both arms parallel to the floor. Hold for 8-10 seconds.

GOALS

1. Core stability and control

2. Hip flexibility, mobility and strength

3. Upper-body and lower-body differentiation

4. Balance and strength

5. Posture control

POSITIVE SIGNS

☐ Able to maintain straight back and posture

☐ Able to keep hips stable

☐ Able to lift hands while maintaining a straight back

NEGATIVE SIGNS

☐ Fidgety

☐ Slouches (e.g., C curve)

☐ Neck and back tension

☐ Pain and discomfort

29) SWING PLANK

MATERIALS: Mat

INSTRUCTIONS:

*Add metronome to work on timing and auditory processing

1. Start in a low plank position, with elbows on the mat and legs extended with toes on the floor.

2. In a controlled manner, dip the hips down toward the mat on one side of the body, then the other side.

3. Repeat 5–7 times, slowly.

GOALS

1. Bilateral coordination

2. Motor planning and timing

3. Crossing the midline

4. Spatial orientation

5. Visual skills (peripheral vision, visual fixation, visual tracking)

6. Body awareness

7. Right- and left-side discrimination

8. Posture and balance

9. Core stability and strength

10. Pelvic (hips) stability

POSITIVE SIGNS

☐ Smooth and coordinated movement patterns

☐ Able to maintain stable hips

☐ Able to twist from side to side while keeping feet and elbows stable on the floor

☐ Able to maintain head control

NEGATIVE SIGNS

☐ Unable to coordinate

☐ Unable to maintain straight posture (e.g., falls)

☐ Unable to twist from side to side

☐ Difficulty differentiating right and left sides of the body

☐ Difficulty timing movement with metronome

☐ Excessive tension and pressure on shoulders, neck and arms

☐ Lack of endurance and strength

30) SIDE PLANK

MATERIALS: Mat

INSTRUCTIONS:

1. Begin seated on the mat, with your knees bent, feet behind you, on your left side, in a "Mermaid" pose.

2. Place your bent left elbow down on the mat, extend your legs to be in line with your body, and lift your hips up off the mat, pushing down on your left elbow. Be sure to keep the body straight.

3. If strong enough, turn your head to the right and dip your hips down toward the mat and back up 3 times.

4. Switch sides and repeat.

5. Frequency: 3-5 times a week.

GOALS

1. Core strength and control

2. Head control

3. Shoulder stability and strength

4. Hand strength

5. Balance and stability

6. Pelvic strength

7. Hip flexibility

POSITIVE SIGNS

☐ Maintaining proper posture and strength on both sides of the body

☐ Able to maintain weight on the weight-bearing arm

☐ Able to lift hips off the floor and stabilize

NEGATIVE SIGNS

☐ Unable to lift hips off the floor

☐ Unable to maintain head control

☐ May fall over

☐ Confusion and frustration

☐ Excessive tension and pressure on the arms

☐ May be holding breath and creating tension on neck

MODIFICATIONS

- Bend one knee and balance; self push off with feet as well as the arm

- Bend elbow instead of keeping it straight

31) BOAT POSE TWIST

MATERIALS: Mat

INSTRUCTIONS:

*Add metronome to work on timing and auditory processing

BEGINNER WITH FEET DOWN

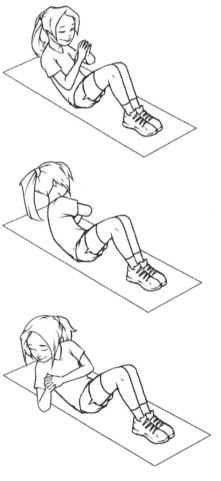

1. Sit down on a mat with knees bent, feet flat on the floor, and hands together.

2. Twist the torso to the left, while keeping feet flat on the floor.

3. Reverse and twist to the right, while keeping feet flat on the floor.

4. Repeat 10 times.

ADVANCED WITH <u>FEET UP</u>

5. Sit down on a mat with knees bent, feet off the floor, and hands together.

6. Twist the torso to the left without moving the legs.

7. Reverse the twist to the right, keeping the legs stable.

8. Repeat 10 times.

GOALS

1. Core strength and stability

2. Later flexibility and strength

3. Pelvis control

4. Lower body strength and stability

5. Neck control and strength

6. Upper-body and lower-body differentiation

7. Right- and left-side discrimination

8. Head control

9. Vestibular input

POSITIVE SIGNS

- ☐ Able to coordinate movements

- ☐ Able to keep feet flat on the floor while the upper body is moving

- ☐ If doing the advanced exercise, able to only move the upper body and keep the legs stable

- ☐ Able to differentiate between the upper and lower body

- ☐ Able to only move from the upper body

- ☐ Able to keep hips level

NEGATIVE SIGNS

- ☐ Unable to maintain balance

- ☐ May slouch

- ☐ May become fidgety

- ☐ Difficulty motor planning

- ☐ Lower body moves with the upper body

- ☐ Difficulty keeping hips stable

- ☐ Low endurance

- ☐ Might feel dizzy or nauseous

CHAPTER 5

ADDITIONAL RECOMMENDATIONS AND RESOURCES

A. HOW DO YOU KNOW IF A TREATMENT PLAN AND EXERCISES ARE WORKING?

Parents often view their children subjectively and have a hard time seeing the gradual changes their children are making with treatment. I created a checklist to help parents more objectively see their child's development. The same list can also be used to determine if the treatment plan is not working. At times, a child may regress, and this should prompt the care provider to change the approach to treatment.

To make this routine easier for non-professionals to implement, I have created an additional list for monitoring progress and a letter of encouragement to parents who are working on the Spinal Galant Reflex with their child. The following list is one that I created with my own children and students. Make sure to add other symptoms and areas that you might observe that I have not included. This list can also include goals you are working on or goals parents have that relate to the Spinal Galant Reflex. What is on the list depends on the individual client, and the goal is to observe and note visible improvements. **After about 6–8 weeks of constant reflex integration exercises, you should begin seeing changes.** If, for any reason, there is **no improvement, go back and examine your treatment plan.**

B. SUGGESTED MOVEMENT BREAKS AND ACTIVITIES TO HELP PROMOTE SPINAL GALANT REFLEX INTEGRATION

To help increase the number of opportunities the child gets to practice, incorporate movement breaks that target the Spinal Galant Reflex throughout the day. One way to do this is by creating the child's movement breaks to address the Spinal Galant Reflex. While creating the child's movement activities, be careful not to frustrate the child by demanding an exercise that is too difficult for them. You want the child to ease into movements and preferably initiate the games themselves. Give the child options. These movement breaks should focus on integrating the Spinal Galant Reflex gently and gradually. Please use your clinical judgment and knowledge of the child while you are creating this plan. Below are the suggested activities to get you started.

TABLE #2: SUGGESTED ACTIVITIES TO INCORPORATE THROUGHOUT THE DAY

VESTIBULAR	STRETCH & FLEXIBILITY
• Resistance Exercise on Hands & Knees • Tail Wag • Twist Jack • Boat Pose Twist • Bicycle Curls • Rolling Like a Ball • Side Jackknives • Supine Heel Tap	• Bear Sit Stretch • Seated Hip Stretch • Standing Leg Stretch • Supine Leg Stretch • Resistance Band Side Steps • Therapy Band Side Bends • Seated Floor Side Bends • Windshield Wipers • Swing Plank
TACTILE	**HIP & PELVIS MOBILITY**
• Rolling Like a Ball • Back Crawl • Therapy Ball Massage • Snow Angel • Supine Heel Tap • Bicycle Curls • Supine Leg Stretch	• Elbow to Hip Squeeze • Pelvic Clock • Hip Circle on Therapy Ball • Bridge Hip Drop • Hula Hoop • Driving a Car • Supine Leg Stretch • Standing Leg Stretch • Plank to Side Taps • Fire Hydrant

Table #2: Suggested Activities to Incorporate Throughout the Day

Visit https://ritp.info/spinal-galant-book for downloadable version.

C. TREATMENT IDEAS FOR OCCUPATIONAL THERAPISTS WORKING IN A CLINICAL SETTING

There are a variety of games and activities you can incorporate to address the Spinal Galant Reflex. The challenge may be grading the activity to meet children at their level while maintaining excitement and fun.

- Most exercises, games and tools in the clinic can directly or indirectly trigger the Spinal Galant Reflex. Use your clinical judgment to set up your treatment session.

- Target the appropriate muscles and ligaments to work on hip and pelvis mobility and strength.

- Consider working closely with a Pelvic Floor Specialist if a child is having bladder control problems and incontinence.

- Incorporate therapy equipment, such as:

    o Swings (e.g., Bolster, Moon Swing, Trapeze, Platform and Frog)

    o Balancing and rocking on a therapy ball

    o Riding on a scooter board

    o Balance boards, etc.

- If you are trained in the following tools, incorporate them in your sessions. Here are some suggestions:

    o Masgutova Method (MNRI)

    o Rhythmic Movement Training (RMTi)

    o Listening programs, such as Integrated Listening Systems (iLs)

    o Interactive Metronome (IM)

    o Brain Gym and other movement exercises you think are beneficial in your clinical settings.

D. LETTER TO PARENT/CAREGIVER

Dear Parents,

When the Spinal Galant Reflex starts to integrate, you will begin to see improvements and changes in your child's development. To make the changes that are needed, however, you should practice the home exercises your occupational therapist assigns for at least 10 minutes per day. If, after six to eight weeks of therapy, you do not see any changes in your child, please contact your occupational therapist. You know your child best and will notice the main areas of growth or lack thereof. To help guide you through the process, here are some things you can look for and observe during your child's treatment:

- Your child may become a lot more coordinated or start to show improvement in movement activities.

- Your child may begin to tumble and roll with ease.

- Your child's seated and standing posture may begin to improve.

- Your child may become stronger and more alert.

- Your child may have better bladder control.

- Your child may become less fidgety.

- Your child might be open to wearing different textures of clothing.

- Your child may be a lot more interested in joining a game or participating in sports (increased confidence).

- Your child may become more focused and less distracted.

- Your child's balance, muscle tone and stability may improve.

- Your child may become stronger (e.g., better trunk and core muscle strength).

- Your child may have better focus and pay more attention.

TABLE #3: SPINAL GALANT REFLEX INTEGRATION EXERCISE LOG

	Spinal Galant Reflex Integration Exercises	Date Introduced	Date Given to Parents	Date Mastered
1	Snow Angel			
2	Tail Wag			
3	Hip Circles on Therapy Ball			
4	Supine Heel Tap			
5	Back Crawl			
6	Therapy Ball Massage			
7	Elbow to Hip Squeeze			
8	Plank to Side Taps			
9	Rolling Like a Ball			
10	Hula Hoop			
11	Bridge Hip Drop			
12	Pelvic Clock			
13	Resistance Band Side Steps			

14	Fire Hydrant			
15	Therapy Band Side Bend			
16	Seated Chair Side Bend			
17	Seated Floor Side Bend			
18	Standing Leg Stretch			
19	Supine Leg Stretch			
20	Side Jackknives			
21	Windshield Wipers			
22	Resistance Exercise on All Fours			
23	Army Crawl			
24	Crawling with Beanbag			
25	Driving a Car			
26	Twist Jacks			
27	Bicycle Curls			
28	Seated Hip Stretch			

29	Swing Plank			
30	Side Plank			
31	Boat Pose Twist			

Visit https://ritp.info/spinal-galant-book for a downloadable version.

GLOSSARY

Agonist Muscles: muscle groups that contract together to create a desired action.

Antagonist Muscles: muscle groups that move against agonist muscles to produce an opposite force.

Asymmetrical Tonic Neck Reflex (ATNR): is a primitive reflex pattern that usually emerges in utero, near 18 weeks, is fully present at birth, and integrates approximately six months after birth. The ATNR is an involuntary movement reaction in response to the head turning to the right or to the left. When the head turns to one side, the ATNR causes the arm and leg the head turns toward to extend (stretch) while the opposite arm and leg flex (bend).

Auditory Localization: the ability to perceive and locate from where a sound is coming.

Binaural Hearing: the ability to hear with both ears equally.

Binocular Vision: also known as **eye teaming,** binocular vision is the ability to use both eyes to focus on an object to see a clear, singular image.

Body Awareness: is the understanding of where our body parts are in space and how they are moving.

Convergence: an inward movement of both eyes to focus on a single object; also called "binocular vision."

Cross-lateral Movements: any movement pattern that requires the use of both parts of the body to coordinate and move simultaneously to execute a purposeful pattern of movements by crossing the midline. Activities such as walking, running and crawling, require us to cross the midline of the body.

Divergence: an outward movement of both eyes to focus on an object further away; also called "binocular" vision.

Extension: straightening of body parts.

Eye-hand Coordination: also known as **hand-eye coordination**, is the ability to process visual input to guide the hands to achieve a specific task (e.g., reaching and grasping).

Eye Teaming: also known as **binocular vision,** is the ability to use both eyes to focus on an object to see a clear, singular image.

Flexion: bending of body parts.

Hip Flexibility: is the ability of the hip joint to move freely and easily in different directions, without discomfort or restriction.

Incontinence: an involuntary loss of urine or feces or the inability to control the timing or frequency of urination or defecation.

Moro Reflex: is a primitive reflex pattern that typically emerges in utero and integrates approximately four months after birth. Moro Reflex is an involuntary reaction to what the brain perceives as an outside threat. The threatening stimuli can come in via touch, sound or the feeling of being dropped, which creates a sense of falling. When the child senses these sensations, the reflex causes the fanning and clenching of fingers, spreading or extending the extremities, followed by a quick flexion of extremities, and crying or anger.

Motor Learning: is a neurological ability to learn new movement skills through practice and repetition.

Motor Planning: is the ability to understand, plan and execute multiple-step movement activities in the correct order.

Movement Overflow: also known as "**motor overflow,**" is an involuntary movement (motor) pattern observed during voluntary activity. For example, the tongue sticking out or facial grimace during handwriting or balancing activities.

Palmer (Grasp) Reflex: is a primitive reflex pattern that emerges in utero at approximately 11 weeks gestation and integrates approximately 12 months after birth. When the infant's palm is stroked or touched at the base of the fingers, the fingers close into a firm grasp starting from the pinky finger.

Peripheral Vision: is an eye's ability to use side vision while gazing straight ahead.

Postural Reflexes: are mature patterns of responses that control balance, motor coordination and sensory-motor development.

Primitive Reflexes: are involuntary movement patterns that are present at birth and become dormant or "integrated" before the child reaches 12 months of age. Most reflexes become integrated into a pattern of movement after infancy, so more mature and voluntary movements can emerge.

Proprioceptive Input: is an internal sense of **body awareness** that comes from our joints, muscles, tendons and connective tissues when we move or bear weight on our limbs.

Retained Reflex: is a term used to refer to primitive reflexes that are active in the body when they should have been inhibited (dormant).

Right/Left Discrimination: is an internal or external spatial perception, interpretation, and differentiation of sensory information that originated from the left and right sides of the body.

Rooting Reflex: is a primitive reflex pattern that typically emerges in utero and integrates approximately three to four months after birth. When the baby's mouth or cheek is stroked or touched, the head turns toward the stroke, and the mouth opens in search of stimuli. If the mouth finds something to grab, the mouth closes over it, and the sucking motion begins.

Saccade Eye Movement: is an eye's ability to accurately jump back and forth between targets.

Scoliosis: an abnormal, lateral curvature of the spine.

Sensory Integration: is a term, developed by Jean Ayers, which explains how the brain receives, perceives and reacts to sensory information either from inside or outside the body. She defines sensory integration as *"the neurological process that organizes sensation from one's own body and from the environment and makes it possible to use the body effectively within the environment."*

Smooth Pursuit: is the eye's ability to smoothly and accurately track a moving object or follow a line.

Spatial Orientation: is the brain's ability to orient the body to the ground with or without vision.

Spinal Galant Reflex: is a primitive reflex pattern present in the womb and also present at birth that integrates at approximately 9-12 months of age. When the right or left side of the back below the waist is stroked or touched, this reflex causes the child to side-bend toward the same direction.

Symmetrical Tonic Neck Reflex (STNR): is a primitive reflex pattern that usually emerges in utero and continues to develop after birth. It becomes active at approximately six months of age and starts to integrate at approximately ten months. The STNR is an involuntary reaction to a downward and upward movement of the head. There are two STNR positions. **Position 1** is a downward head movement, which causes the elbows to flex and the legs to extend. **Position 2** is an upward head movement (also called Sphinx Position), which causes the elbows to extend and the legs to flex.

Tonic Labyrinthine Reflex (TLR): is a primitive reflex pattern that usually emerges in utero and continues to develop after birth. The TLR is an involuntary reaction to the forward and backward movement of the head. There are two types: **TLR Forward** occurs when the head is in front of the spine, causing the arms and legs to flex and tuck inward. **TLR Backward** occurs when the head is behind the line of the spine, causing the arms and the legs to extend, and the back to arch and stiffen.

Vestibular Sense: is the body's sense of balance and movement.

Visual Discrimination: is the ability to recognize details in what is being seen while identifying similarities and differences.

Visual Tracking: is the ability to maintain a visual gaze on a moving object or a predictable line while reading.

RESOURCES

Active Baby, Healthy Brain: 135 Fun Exercises to Maximize Your Child's Brain Development from Birth through age 5½, by Margaret Sasse.

Assessing Neuromotor Readiness for Learning: The INPP Developmental Screening Test and School Intervention Programme, by Sally Goddard.

Integration of Infant Dynamic and Postural Reflex Patterns-MNRI (Masgutova Neurosensorimotor Reflex Integration), by Svetlana Rihanna Masgutova Ketubah, PhD.

Masgutova Neurosensorimotor Reflex Integration Programs https://masgutovamethod.com/

Movements That Heal, by Harald Blomberg, MD and Moira Dempsy.

Neuromotor Immaturity in Children and Adults: The INPP Screening Test for Clinicians and Health Practitioners, by Sally Goddard.

Parents' Guide to Masgutova Neurosensorimotor Reflex Integration (MNRI), by Svetlana Masgutova, PhD & Denis Masgutova.

Reflexes, Learning and Behavior, by Sally Goddard.

The Misunderstood Child: Understanding and Coping with Your Child's Learning Disabilities, by Larry B. Silver, MD.

The Out-of-Sync Child: Recognizing and Coping with Sensory Integration Dysfunction, by Carol Stock Kranowitz, MA.

The Rhythmic Movement Method: A Revolutionary Approach to Improved Health and Well-Being, by Harald Blomberg, MD.

The Symphony of Reflexes: Interventions for Human Development, Autism, CP, and Other Neurological Disorders, by Bonnie L. Brandes, Med.

Medical Dictionary: https://medical-dictionary.thefreedictionary.com/

ABOUT THE AUTHOR

Kokeb Girma McDonald is a pediatric occupational therapist and the founder of the Reflex Integration Through Play™ (RITP) program. She is the mother of two wonderful children, and has extensive professional experience working with young people of all ages and backgrounds since 2004. Recognizing the need for practical and universally accessible primitive-reflex-integration programs, Kokeb created the *Integrating Primitive Reflexes Through Play and Exercise* book series and the Reflex Integration Through Play™ method to empower and reassure frustrated parents, and to offer fellow professionals a tool to expand their clinical reach. Kokeb's formal education includes a Bachelor's of Science in Occupational Therapy, and a Master's of Science in Health Care Administration, Management, and Change in Health Care Options. She also has additional training in Masgutova Neurosensorimotor Reflex Integration (MNRI), Integrated Listening Systems (iLs), Interactive Metronome (IM), and Rhythmic Movement Training (RMTi).

Make a Difference
by leaving a review!

Instructions: Scan the code above, scroll to the bottom of the Amazon product page, and click the "Write a Review" button

Your review helps Reflex Integration Through Play™ reach more parents, therapists, and teachers in need!

I appreciate all of your feedback and love hearing what you have to say. These books are for you! We need your help to make our series better. Thank you for all your support!

Kokeb Mcdonald

OTR/L & Author